THE MAGIC HOURGLASS

A TIME-TRAVEL ADVENTURE GAME

HEATHER MAISNER   illustrated by PETER JOYCE

WALKER BOOKS
LONDON

TIME CHART

Read the instructions opposite before you start to play.

	PAGES	DATES		REMARKABLE MOMENTS
white	7	THE PRESENT		All games begin and end here!
purple	8 and 9	THE 19TH CENTURY	1800—1899	THE EIFFEL TOWER · THE WAGON TRAIN GOES WEST
pink	10 and 11	THE 18TH CENTURY	1700—1799	AUSTRALIA AT LAST! · PETER THE GREAT
pale yellow	12 and 13	THE 17TH CENTURY	1600—1699	A RICH AND BUSY CITY · LAND OF THE SAMURAI
pale blue	14 and 15	THE 16TH CENTURY	1500—1599	A RENAISSANCE CITY · EMPIRE OF THE INCAS
green	16 and 17	THE 15TH CENTURY	1400—1499	COLUMBUS IN TROUBLE · LAND AHOY! WHERE ARE WE?
turquoise	18 and 19	THE 14TH CENTURY	1300—1399	A COLD AND DRAUGHTY CASTLE · CITY OF GOLD
grey	20 and 21	THE 13TH CENTURY	1200—1299	THE ROOF OF THE WORLD · MARCO POLO
dark blue	22 and 23	THE 9TH CENTURY	800—899	A VIKING WINTER · INDIA IN THE RAINS
brown	24 and 25	THE 2ND CENTURY AD	100—199	A DAY AT THE RACES · SILK AND SECRETS
red	26 and 27	1000—2000 BC		IN THE VALLEY OF THE KINGS · CIRCLE OF STONE
pale orange	28 and 29	65—136 MILLION YEARS AGO		LORDS OF THE LAND · LORDS OF SEA AND SKY

~ OBJECTS FROM THE PRESENT ~

No Entry sign	telephone wires	television	car
toilet roll	office block	electric drill	outboard boat engine
bicycle	wristwatch	binoculars	electric kettle
toaster	traffic light	lawn mower	camera
radio	Anglepoise lamp	motorbike	traffic cone

Great Aunt Fantasia, a famous historian, has sent you a magic HOURGLASS and this letter.

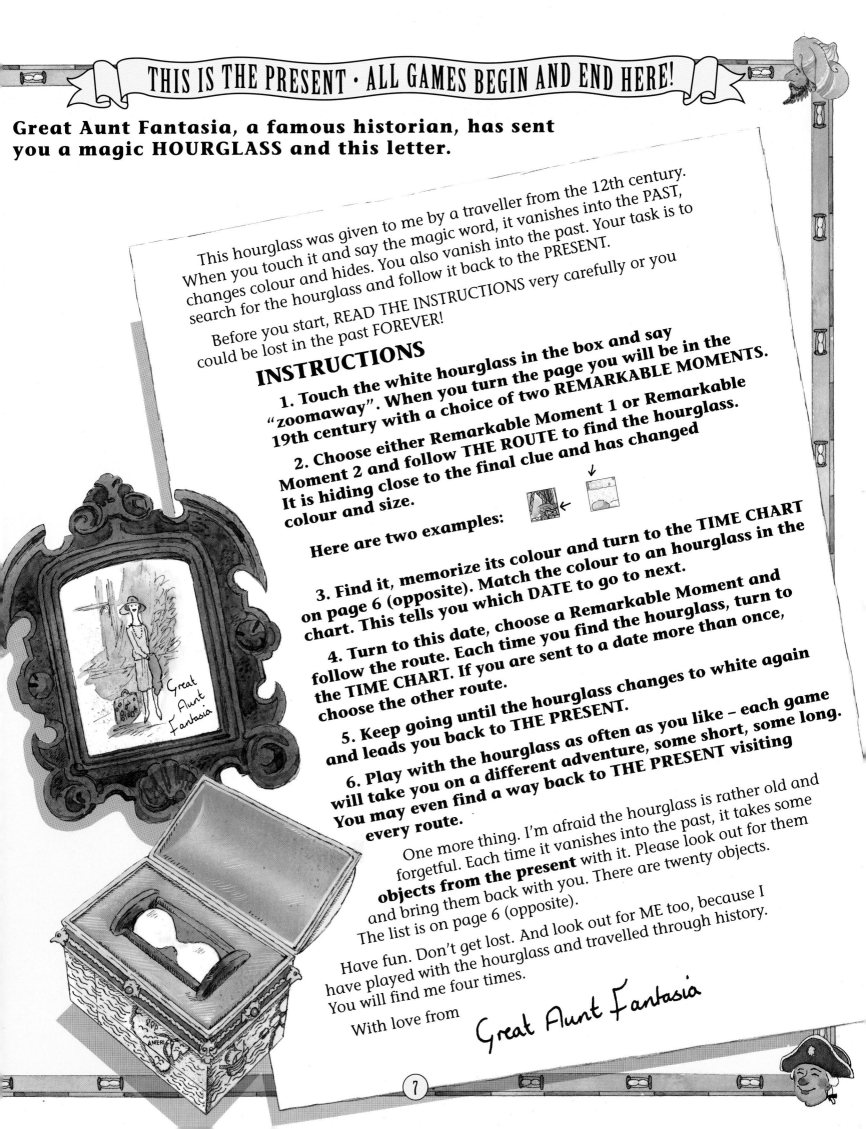

This hourglass was given to me by a traveller from the 12th century. When you touch it and say the magic word, it vanishes into the PAST, changes colour and hides. You also vanish into the past. Your task is to search for the hourglass and follow it back to the PRESENT.

Before you start, READ THE INSTRUCTIONS very carefully or you could be lost in the past FOREVER!

INSTRUCTIONS

1. Touch the white hourglass in the box and say "zoomaway". When you turn the page you will be in the 19th century with a choice of two REMARKABLE MOMENTS.

2. Choose either Remarkable Moment 1 or Remarkable Moment 2 and follow THE ROUTE to find the hourglass. It is hiding close to the final clue and has changed colour and size.

Here are two examples:

3. Find it, memorize its colour and turn to the TIME CHART on page 6 (opposite). Match the colour to an hourglass in the chart. This tells you which DATE to go to next.

4. Turn to this date, choose a Remarkable Moment and follow the route. Each time you find the hourglass, turn to the TIME CHART. If you are sent to a date more than once, choose the other route.

5. Keep going until the hourglass changes to white again and leads you back to THE PRESENT.

6. Play with the hourglass as often as you like – each game will take you on a different adventure, some short, some long. You may even find a way back to THE PRESENT visiting every route.

One more thing. I'm afraid the hourglass is rather old and forgetful. Each time it vanishes into the past, it takes some **objects from the present** with it. Please look out for them and bring them back with you. There are twenty objects. The list is on page 6 (opposite).

Have fun. Don't get lost. And look out for ME too, because I have played with the hourglass and travelled through history. You will find me four times.

With love from *Great Aunt Fantasia*

THE EIFFEL TOWER

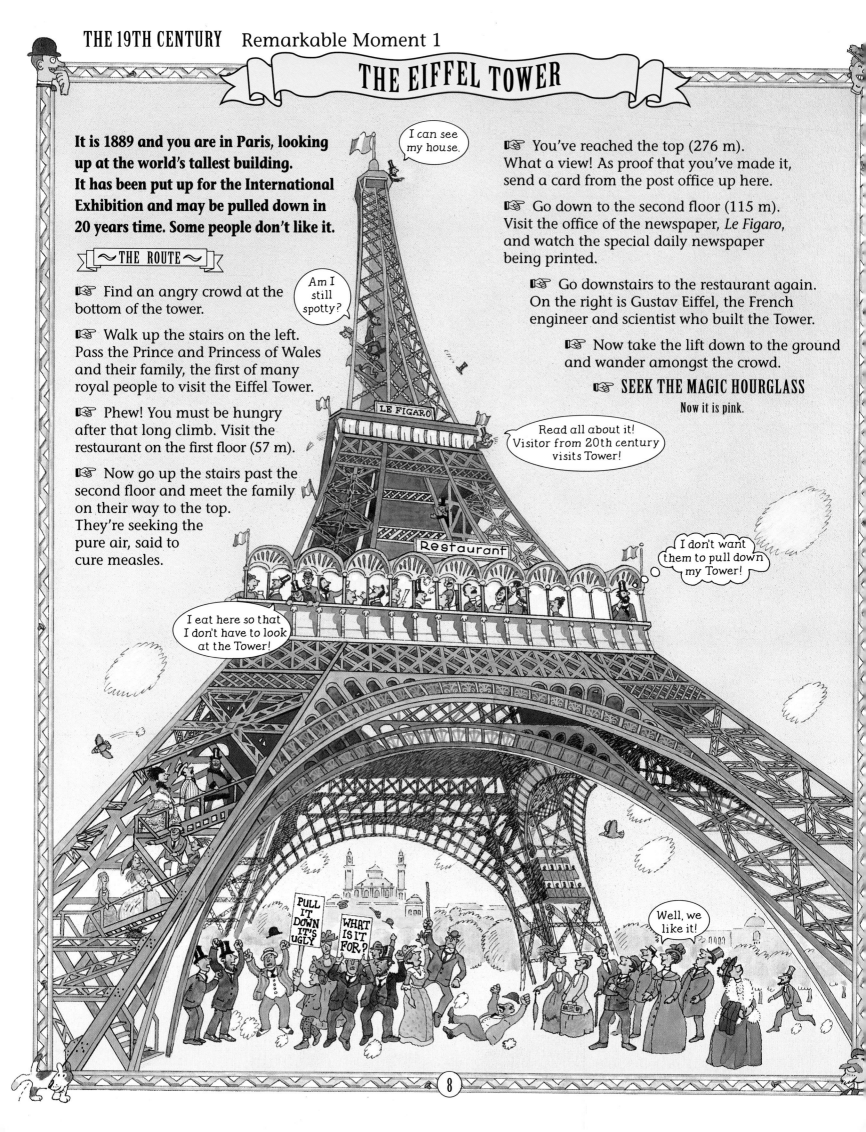

It is 1889 and you are in Paris, looking up at the world's tallest building. It has been put up for the International Exhibition and may be pulled down in 20 years time. Some people don't like it.

~ THE ROUTE ~

☞ Find an angry crowd at the bottom of the tower.

☞ Walk up the stairs on the left. Pass the Prince and Princess of Wales and their family, the first of many royal people to visit the Eiffel Tower.

☞ Phew! You must be hungry after that long climb. Visit the restaurant on the first floor (57 m).

☞ Now go up the stairs past the second floor and meet the family on their way to the top. They're seeking the pure air, said to cure measles.

☞ You've reached the top (276 m). What a view! As proof that you've made it, send a card from the post office up here.

☞ Go down to the second floor (115 m). Visit the office of the newspaper, *Le Figaro*, and watch the special daily newspaper being printed.

☞ Go downstairs to the restaurant again. On the right is Gustav Eiffel, the French engineer and scientist who built the Tower.

☞ Now take the lift down to the ground and wander amongst the crowd.

☞ **SEEK THE MAGIC HOURGLASS**

Now it is pink.

THE WAGON TRAIN GOES WEST

You're in America as the pioneers trek west on the Oregon Trail. They hope to find a better life in green and fertile Oregon, 3,000 km away. The journey, across prairies, deserts and mountains, will take four to six months.

~ THE ROUTE ~

☞ Join the last wagon in the line. Families travel together for safety. Wagons are crowded with tools, clothes, linen and food. You won't see a store for months.

☞ Pass the next wagon and find a runaway iron tyre. It's so hot and dry that the wooden wheel has shrunk and the tyre has rolled off.

☞ Thirsty? Move on to the circle of wagons where women are washing dishes in leftover cold tea. Ask them for a drink.

☞ Stop by the ox too tired to stand. Many people and animals die on the long journey west.

☞ You're at the river. Cross carefully. When the river is swollen, people can get swept away.

☞ Join the men chasing buffalo. They haven't tasted fresh meat for weeks. Buffalo skins are dried for rawhide and tanned for leather.

☞ Look up at the cliffs on the right. These people sending smoke signals are Plains Indians. There are many tribes with different languages who have lived here for thousands of years.

☞ Ride ahead to the scout, checking the route for dangers. He's a Mountain Man and has made the western wilderness his home.

☞ **SEEK THE MAGIC HOURGLASS**
Now it is pale yellow.

AUSTRALIA AT LAST!

It is 1770 and you are with Captain James Cook and his crew, who have just set foot in Australia for the first time. They have come on a scientific voyage from Britain and are exploring the east coast.

~ THE ROUTE ~

☞ Find Captain Cook's ship, the *Endeavour*. The crew survived the incredibly long voyage here because he made sure that they ate well and that the ship was kept clean.

☞ Row ashore. Cook calls this Botany Bay as there are so many fascinating plants growing here.

☞ Hungry? Help the sailors carry two huge stingray up the beach for lunch.

☞ Now step across to Captain Cook, who is drawing a map. Other explorers have sighted this land before, but Cook is the first to map the east coast.

☞ Cross the beach and meet the two artists. They are drawing plants and animals, as cameras have not yet been invented.

☞ Do you see the man hoisting a flag? Cook is claiming this land for Britain and will call it New South Wales.

☞ Oh dear, someone has fallen into the bushes! It is a scientist collecting plants to take home.

☞ Walk past the kangaroo to meet the Aborigines. They have been here for thousands of years. Their religion is called the "Dreamtime". They believe that plants, animals, people and the landscape are all part of nature. This links them to the land in a very special way.

☞ **SEEK THE MAGIC HOURGLASS**
Now it is green.

PETER THE GREAT

You are in St Petersburg, Russia. Tsar Peter the Great has built his new capital city on marshy swampland in the Gulf of Finland. He wants to modernize Russia and impress the rest of the world. This is Peterhof, his new palace and park.

~ THE ROUTE ~

☞ Start at the palace at the top. Peter planned the park with the help of foreign architects. Soldiers and peasants built it.

☞ Walk down the steps beside the fountains and along the main canal as far as the rabbit.

☞ Lend a hand to two foreign ambassadors digging the garden. Peter makes his guests work hard. Then he invites them to a banquet.

☞ Walk on to the Adam fountain. Peter also plans to build trick fountains that will spurt water at you.

☞ Go towards the sea and join Peter at his desk. Be as quiet as possible. Peter is editing Russia's first newspaper. He's also a carpenter and shipbuilder.

☞ Walk along the shore behind the peasant. He is carrying earth in his clothes because there are no wheelbarrows. Many peasants have died building St Petersburg.

☞ Lend your jacket to the noble-woman shivering by the sea. She has had to leave the comfort of her home in Moscow for this cold city which is often flooded.

☞ Follow the dogs and meet the nobleman with a beard. Peter makes all noblemen shave or pay a heavy tax. The man's medallion shows that he has paid the tax.

☞ Stop and talk to Catherine, who is holding a parasol. She is Peter's second wife. Before she married him she was a peasant. Now he has made her Empress.

☞ **SEEK THE MAGIC HOURGLASS**
Now it is pale yellow.

A RICH AND BUSY CITY

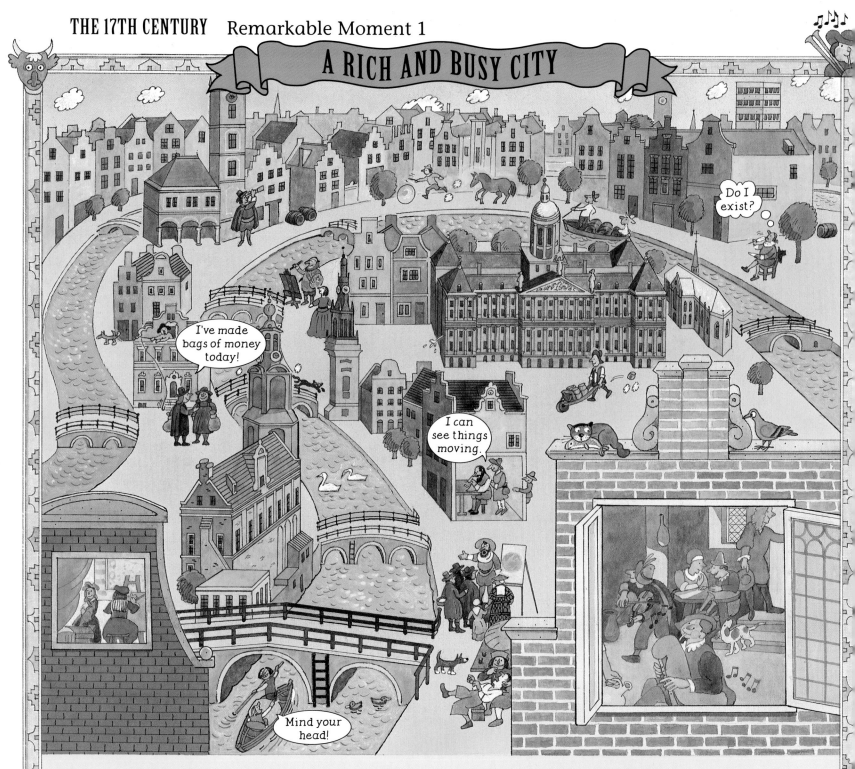

You are in Amsterdam. This city is growing richer every day from fishing, shipping, banking and trade with the rest of the world.

~ THE ROUTE ~

☞ Find two merchants taking bags of money to the new Bank of Amsterdam.

☞ Follow the black cat across the bridge over the canal. Canals have been built to drain the marshy land so that merchants can build more houses.

☞ Turn left and meet the artist by the canal. He's Rembrandt van Rijn, the great Dutch painter. Today he's painting a portrait.

☞ Cross the nearest bridge and join the man looking through a telescope. Telescopes have recently been invented by a Dutch spectacle-maker, who calls them "lookers".

☞ Walk along the canal bank, past the horse and the boat to the man deep in thought. He's a foreign philosopher who can publish ideas here that are not liked in his own country.

☞ Cross the next bridge and run past the cheese-seller with the barrow in front of the new Town Hall. 13,659 long wooden stakes have been driven into the marshy soil to support this building.

☞ Stop and look through the latest Dutch microscope. See germs for the very first time.

☞ Join the man with a map of the world. He is Abel Janszoon Tasman, a Dutch explorer and the first European to have reached New Zealand.

☞ **SEEK THE MAGIC HOURGLASS**
Now it is green.

LAND OF THE SAMURAI

You have arrived in Japan, where the *shogun* – military leader – is ruler. Go carefully. Foreigners may not enter the country and no Japanese may leave.

～ THE ROUTE ～

☞ Follow the *samurai* over the bridge. Japan is divided into three classes with the *samurai* at the top. *Samurai* wear two swords, are brave and loyal and have the power to put you to death.

☞ Slip past the *ninja*, waiting at the gate. He is a spy trained to kill enemies.

☞ Turn left. Dart in front of the oxen pulling the *shogun's* wheeled carriage. Most people must travel on foot, or in a carriage called a *kago* carried by men.

☞ Slow down! Poet Matsuo Bashō is working on a poem. His short poems about nature are called *haiku*. In Japanese they have three lines and 17 syllables.

☞ Wander through the houses, past the fan-seller to the man flying a kite.

☞ Wave to the woman planting rice in flooded paddy fields. Rice is like money. You use it to pay taxes.

☞ Turn back and join the young ladies at the pond. Stop and admire the cherry blossom.

☞ Continue round the pond, slip through the gate and watch the *samurai* practising archery. Graceful movements count as much as hitting the bull's-eye!

☞ Follow the white cat and *samurai* into the house for the tea ceremony. Bow as you enter. Drink elegantly. This special event makes you calm and content.

☞ **SEEK THE MAGIC HOURGLASS**
Now it is turquoise.

A RENAISSANCE CITY

You have arrived in Italy at the time of the Renaissance, a period of great learning. This is the prosperous city-state of Florence.

～THE ROUTE～

☞ Find artists showing two portraits to wealthy patrons. Patrons help artists by giving them money and telling them what to paint.

☞ Look up at someone about to test a model of Leonardo da Vinci's flying machine. Leonardo is an artist, scientist and inventor.

☞ Follow the horse and cart carrying sacks of raw fleece through the city to the River Arno. Here it will be washed, spun, woven into cloth and then dyed. The cloth industry has made the city rich.

☞ Move on to the woman reading a book beside the river. Before the recent German invention of the printing press, books were copied by hand.

☞ Pass the man in green on the bridge. He is jotting down ideas for *The Prince*, a famous book about power and politics. His name is Niccolò Machiavelli.

☞ Run past the pig and on to the musicians. They have been hired by Leonardo da Vinci to make the Mona Lisa smile as he paints her portrait.

☞ Go past the bear on the bridge and find artist Michelangelo. He is working on his statue of *David*, almost 5 m tall.

☞ Join the man standing in front of the domed cathedral. The huge dome was built by architect Brunelleschi, using new and old building techniques.

☞ **SEEK THE MAGIC HOURGLASS**
Now it is white.

EMPIRE OF THE INCAS

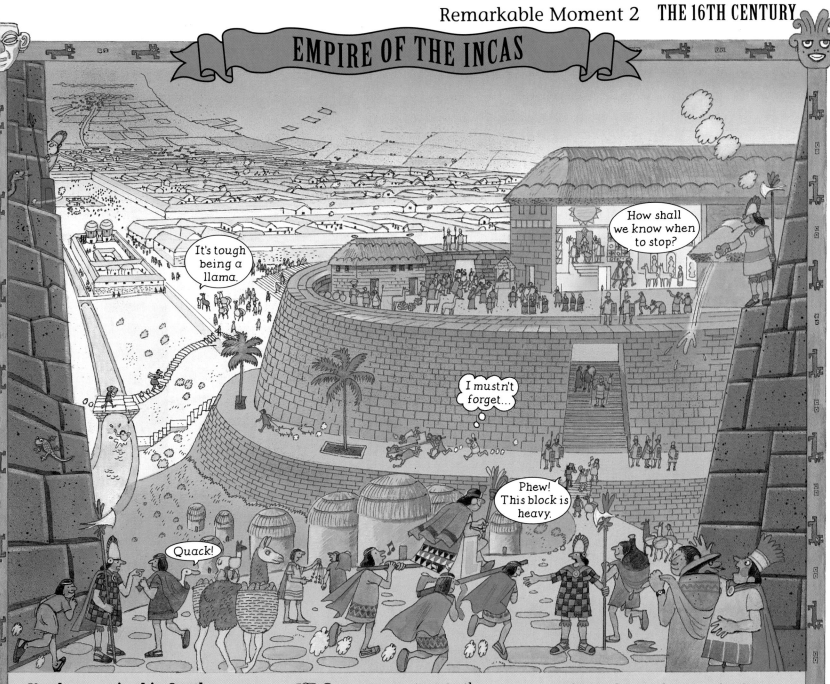

You have arrived in South America at Cuzco, capital of the Inca Empire. This vast and powerful empire stretches from Colombia in the north to Chile in the south.

∼ THE ROUTE ∼

☞ Find the man entering the city to deliver a duck. He is telling the guard the reason for his visit. Only the Inca nobility, including priests and officials, live in Cuzco.

☞ Meet the official who is tying knots in a string called a *quipu*. He records supplies of food, clothes, weapons and tools.

☞ Go up some steps to the man carrying a block of stone. The Incas build perfect stone walls without using cement.

☞ Carry on up to the Golden Enclosure of the Sun Temple. Inside is a large image of the sun made in gold.

☞ See the Emperor sitting on a pedestal? Approach him backwards as a sign of respect. He is said to be descended from the Sun God.

☞ Run back down to the man with the block. Turn and pass the runner. He has memorized his message as there is no written language. Relay runners carry messages along the Inca's 25,000 km of roads.

☞ Hot? Join the man bathing in the clear waters of the river. All the streets are paved, and stone-lined channels bring water and clear away sewage.

☞ Climb onto the bridge and go up the steps to the group of llamas carrying goods. There are no wheeled vehicles, and llamas are the Incas' only pack animals. They are also used for religious sacrifice.

☞ Walk on to the building by the river. It is the Emperor's palace. Inside it is richly decorated with silver and precious stones.

☞ **SEEK THE MAGIC HOURGLASS**
Now it is pink.

COLUMBUS IN TROUBLE

It is 1492 and you are on board Christopher Columbus's ship, the *Santa Maria*. Columbus is trying to reach the East Indies from Spain by sailing west around the world. You have been at sea for five weeks and still haven't seen land.

～ THE ROUTE ～

☞ Find the sailor who has joined the crew to avoid going to prison.

☞ Walk towards the front of the ship and watch Columbus trying to calm the crew. They want to go home.

☞ Walk on. Step over sailors sleeping on deck, the only place they can find.

☞ Climb down the ladder to the storeroom, holding your nose. There are no bathrooms on board so both the ship and the crew stink!

☞ Help the steward check the food supplies and then quickly go back on deck.

☞ Climb up to the crow's-nest and talk to the sailor on look-out duty. Feel the ship roll.

☞ Go down again. Join the sailor who is looking in the sea for signs of land.

☞ **SEEK THE MAGIC HOURGLASS**
Now it is turquoise.

LAND AHOY! WHERE ARE WE?

You are on board the *Niña*, one of two small ships accompanying Christopher Columbus on his voyage. The other ship is the *Pinta*.

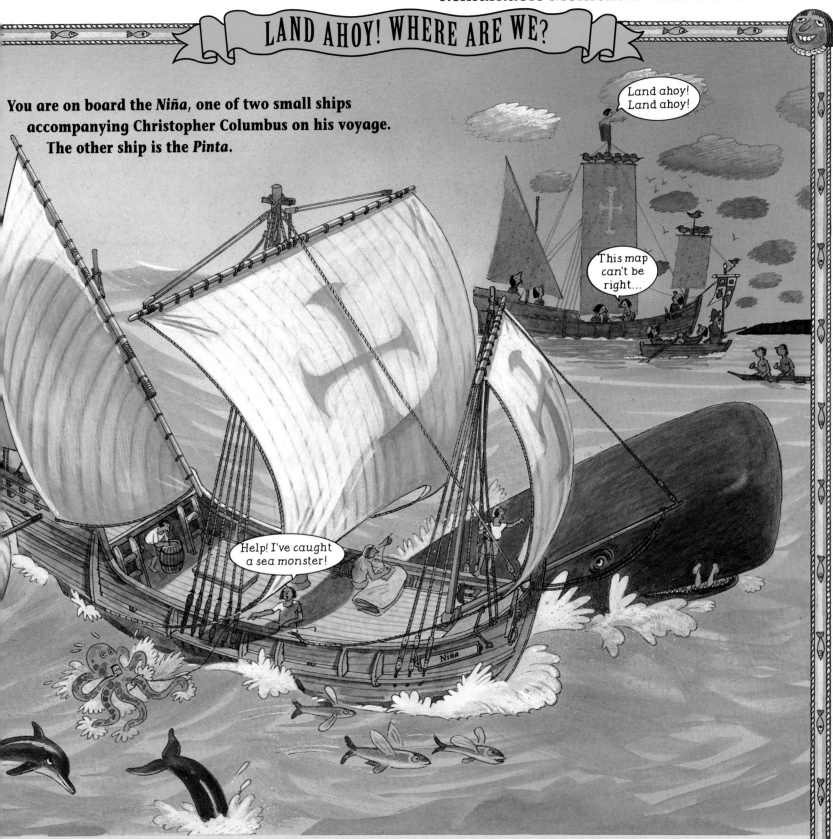

~ THE ROUTE ~

☞ Find the sailor at the water barrel. He is very thirsty, but after five weeks at sea the barrel is empty.

☞ Step across to help the hungry sailor who is fishing.

☞ Cross to the sail-maker, mending sail damaged in a storm.

☞ Swim across to the other ship, the *Pinta*. Mind the whale!

☞ Go aboard. Meet Captain Martin Pinzón, who is trying to check the route on a map of the world.

☞ Climb up the mast. Hurrah! The sailor on look-out duty has spotted land.

☞ Climb down quickly, lower the boat and row towards the shore. Columbus thinks this is the East Indies. In fact it is an island in the Bahamas.

☞ Pass Taino Indians in a canoe. They wonder who you are.

☞ **SEEK THE MAGIC HOURGLASS**
Now it is dark blue.

A COLD AND DRAUGHTY CASTLE

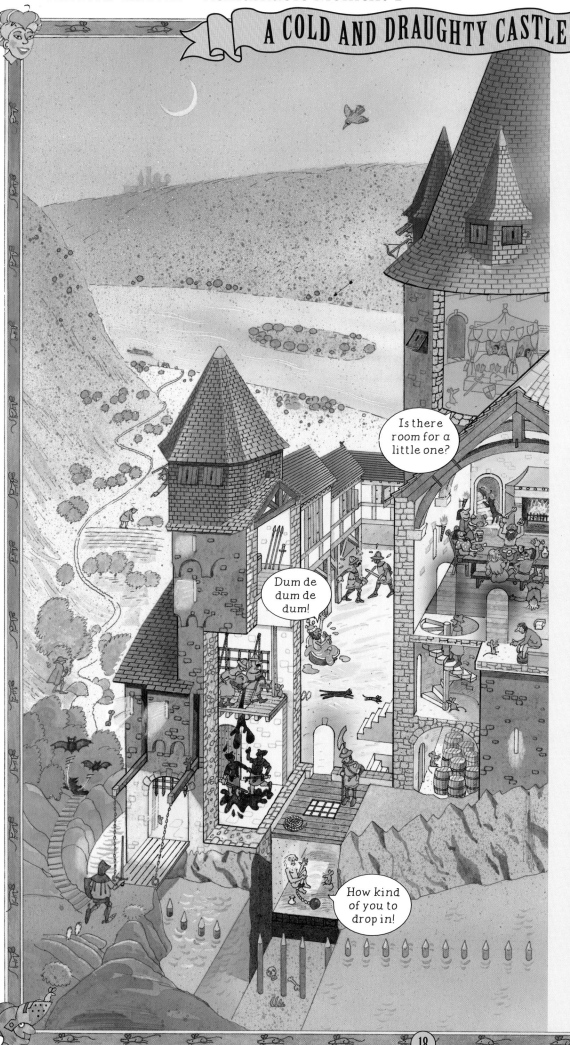

You are beside the Rhine, a major river that winds through the vast German Empire. The Emperor is in power, but princes, nobles and bishops fight for control of the land. Princes live in castles for safety and to show off their wealth.

~ THE ROUTE ~

☞ Start at the river. Goods are transported along the river by barge because the roads are rough and full of danger.

☞ Follow the road to the castle. Wave to the soldier in the tower. He spies on passing boats which have to pay a toll for using this stretch of river.

☞ Cross the drawbridge, but don't fall into the moat. Pointed stakes are there to trap you.

☞ Enter the castle and go through to the yard to meet the Prince. He is bathing in a tub. It's often warmer outside than inside this cold castle.

☞ Climb the winding stairs and join people at the long table. Sit with your back to the fire, the only place to keep warm. Use hard bread for a plate, and eat with a knife and your fingers.

☞ Feeling sleepy? Follow the cat chasing a mouse upstairs to bed. Draw the curtains for privacy and warmth. Is someone else in bed? Don't worry. Guests often sleep together!

☞ Now go downstairs again and visit the guard watching the prisoner. Hold your nose. The castle stinks; soon it will get so bad that the Prince will have to move away for at least two years.

☞ Look out! Too late! You've fallen through the trap door into the dungeon.

☞ SEEK THE MAGIC HOURGLASS. Now it is dark blue.

CITY OF GOLD

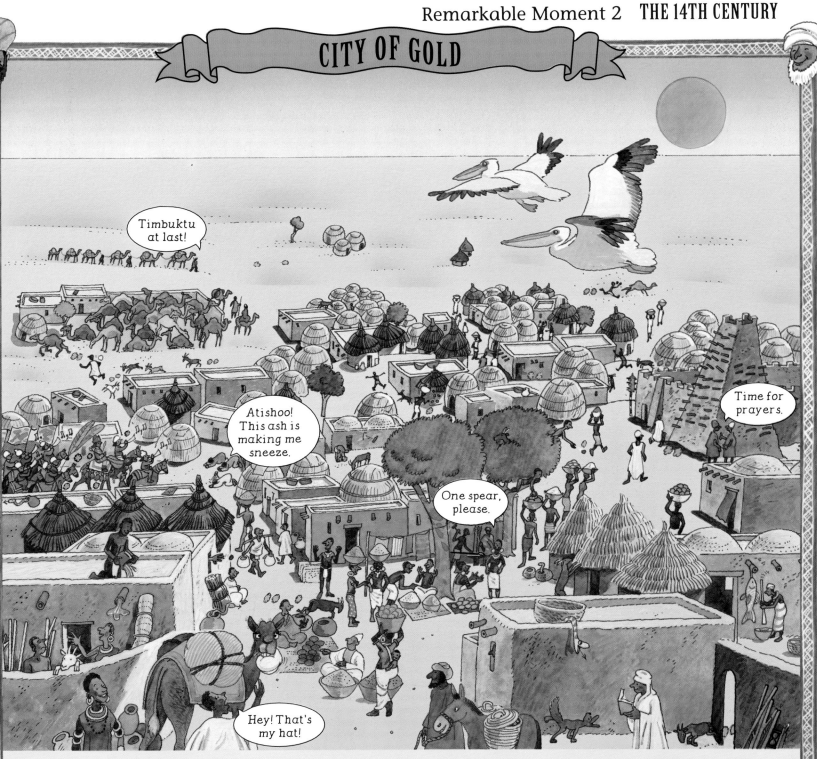

You are in Timbuktu in the wealthy empire of Mali. This city south of the Sahara Desert is the centre of trade in West Africa.

~ THE ROUTE ~

☞ Find the line of camels carrying salt from the north to be exchanged here for gold from the south.

☞ Follow the goats past the camel park. Sometimes there are as many as 4,000 camels here.

☞ Stop by three men bowing to Mansa Musa, the powerful Emperor riding on a camel. He controls the gold, which goes all over the world. Heap ashes on your head as a sign of respect.

☞ Move on to explore the market place. People here don't use money. They exchange goods instead.

☞ Step across to the blacksmith under the trees. He is hammering spears for the Emperor's large army. Soldiers protect the empire and have made the city safe.

☞ It's time for prayers. Join the two men outside the mosque, the Muslim place of worship. The Emperor and many merchants are Muslim.

☞ Hungry? Find the woman who is pounding grain with a long stick. People eat millet, rice, yams, fish, meat and beans.

☞ Now join the man reading a book in Arabic. Timbuktu is famous as a place of learning.

☞ **SEEK THE MAGIC HOURGLASS**
Now it is brown.

THE ROOF OF THE WORLD

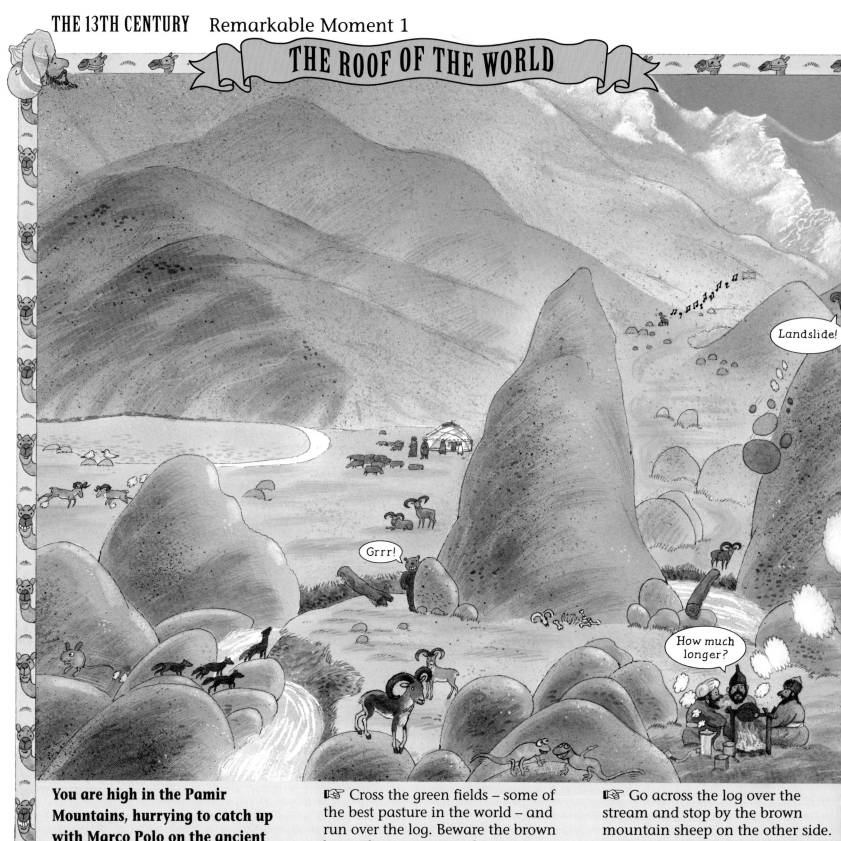

You are high in the Pamir Mountains, hurrying to catch up with Marco Polo on the ancient Silk Road. This is the major trade route between China and the West.

~ THE ROUTE ~

☞ Start at the lake on the left.

☞ Go to the *yurt*, a tent made with goat or camel hair felt. It belongs to nomads, who move from place to place with their animals.

☞ Cross the green fields – some of the best pasture in the world – and run over the log. Beware the brown bear. There are many dangers in these wild mountains.

☞ Find a pile of bones left by wolves. Travellers have put them there to show that you're on the right path.

☞ Hungry? Join travellers cooking over an open fire. Be patient. At this height, fires burn less brightly and food takes longer to cook.

☞ Go across the log over the stream and stop by the brown mountain sheep on the other side. Look at his long horns! Shepherds use them to make bowls and fences

☞ Run ahead to the man playing tunes on a flute. Sing along to keep up your spirits. Ahead lie many bleak and frightening deserts. One is called the Takla Makan. Its name means, "if you go in, you'll never come out".

☞ **SEEK THE MAGIC HOURGLASS**
Now it is pale blue.

MARCO POLO

You have joined Marco Polo on the ancient Silk Road. He is with travellers carrying gold and precious stones to China.

～THE ROUTE～

☞ Join the back of the line of camels.

☞ Meet Marco Polo in the green robe and striped cloak. People have travelled this route for many years but he will be the first European to write about it.

☞ Move ahead to Marco's father carrying a golden tablet. This is a gift from Kublai Khan, ruler of the Mongol Empire, which includes China. It says that the Polos must be given help anywhere in his empire.

☞ Pass Marco's uncle, with a black beard and a long red robe. He is carrying holy oil, a gift to Kublai Khan from the Pope in Italy.

☞ Find two men putting up a signpost to Cathay, the word for China. It's easy to lose your way in the desert.

☞ Quick! Catch the runaway camels. They wear bells to prevent them from getting lost. Camels are ideal for desert travel, as they can go without water for days.

☞ Listen! Can you hear swords clashing? Can you see people fighting in the distance? This is a trick the desert plays on your senses.

☞ Run to the water hole where two camels are resting. Drink up. You won't find water again for hours.

☞ **SEEK THE MAGIC HOURGLASS**
Now it is purple.

A VIKING WINTER

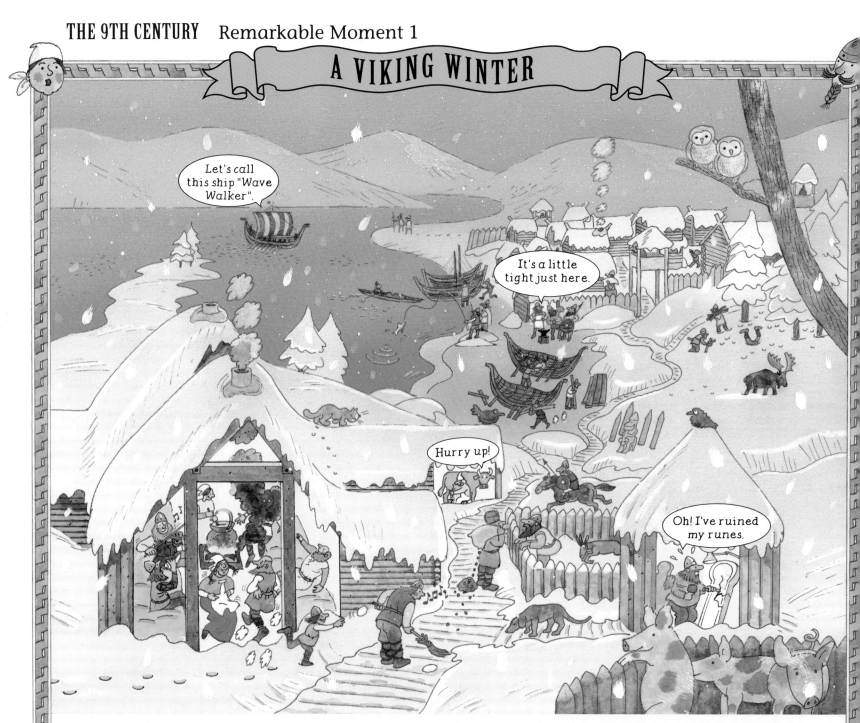

It's winter in Scandinavia, home of the Vikings. These Northmen are mainly farmers but there isn't enough land for them all. The men are building ships so that when the weather is fair, they can go raiding and trading overseas.

~ THE ROUTE ~

☞ Find the man using a hammer and chisel to carve a rune-stone. Runes are stick-like letters with magical meanings. Rune-stones are set up as monuments to the dead.

☞ Walk past the dog and along the path to the girl milking a cow. Girls learn how to sew and cook, make butter and cheese, spin, weave, ride, swim and use weapons. When the men are away, the women run the farms.

☞ Continue along the path to the statue of Thor on the right, one of the many gods and goddesses worshipped by the Vikings. Thor is god of thunder and lightning. The day Thursday is named after him.

☞ Run ahead to help the *thralls* collecting firewood on the right. Vikings are divided into three groups, with *thralls* – slaves – at the bottom.

☞ Now wander through the houses and back along the shore to the two boys catching fish. Boys are sometimes sent to live with other families. This helps prevent family feuds.

☞ Step across to the blacksmith, where the *jarl* – leader – is trying on a piece of armour. It is a *byrnie*, a shirt made of thousands of iron rings.

☞ Now lend a hand to the men building oak longships. These ships can travel huge distances at great speed.

☞ Cold and hungry? Go back past the cow and on to the longhouse, where a woman is cooking over an open fire.

☞ **SEEK THE MAGIC HOURGLASS**
Now it is red.

INDIA IN THE RAINS

You have arrived at a village in India, a vast land divided into many states. It is the time of the monsoon, the wind that brings the heavy rains, making the parched earth green and alive.

~ THE ROUTE ~

☞ Find the herdsman guarding the cattle and playing a bamboo flute to keep himself awake. Cattle are a sign of wealth.

☞ Beware the tiger on your left. Villages are fenced to keep out wild animals.

☞ Follow the man with a stick into the village. He is a *brahmin*. Society is divided into four groups or castes, with *brahmins* – priests and men of learning – at the top.

☞ Turn right then left. Can you smell delicious spiced vegetables? This woman is a vegetarian; she believes life is sacred and animals should not be killed for food.

☞ Move on to the holy man sitting on his own. Put some food in his bowl. Holy men are treated with great respect.

☞ Skip past the snake-charmer under the trees and stop at the well. Water is precious. It is needed to irrigate the fields during the long dry season after the monsoon.

☞ Pass the cart rumbling through the village and join people watching the dancers. Each movement of hands, feet, neck and eyes has a meaning.

☞ Go on to the Hindu temple. Hindus believe all living creatures will live again on earth after they die. Your next life will be a better one if you follow special rules now.

☞ **SEEK THE MAGIC HOURGLASS** Now it is brown.

You've taken too much water.

Mmmm. That smells delicious.

I do hope he is a vegetarian!

I love this tune!

A DAY AT THE RACES

You have arrived in Rome, capital of the mighty Roman Empire, which rules over the western world from Britain to North Africa, and parts of the Middle East. This is the Circus Maximus, the stadium where chariot races are held.

~ THE ROUTE ~

☞ Find the man with a bunch of grapes. He is one of the cheering crowd of 250,000 spectators.

☞ Run down the steps to meet the supporters of the Reds. All drivers belong to one of four teams, which are known by their colours: the Reds, Whites, Greens and Blues.

☞ Move left to greet the Emperor in the royal box. He likes people to come to the races because it makes them happy and this keeps them loyal.

☞ Now join the supporters of the Greens. The front rows are reserved for senators and knights. Everyone comes to the stadium and bets on the races.

☞ Find the Reds chariot driven by the champion. Most drivers are slaves, but he has won over a thousand races and is now as rich and famous as a film star.

☞ Dash across the track to the centre of the stadium. It is about 200 m wide and 600 m long. Each race is seven laps.

☞ Quick! Help carry the Blues driver on a stretcher to safety. Drivers have collided and been thrown from their chariots. This is a dangerous sport. Many men and horses are injured on the track.

☞ Join the line of guards in front of the Blues' supporters at the far side of the stadium.

☞ **SEEK THE MAGIC HOURGLASS** Now it is red.

SILK AND SECRETS

You have arrived in China, the greatest power in Asia. It is the time of the Han Dynasty, when silk and other luxuries are traded across Asia as far as Rome. This is a wealthy man's house.

~ THE ROUTE ~

☞ Find the horse and carriage in the small courtyard. Look up at the sloping roofs of the house. They are said to keep away evil spirits which move in straight lines.

☞ Come through the arch and find the boy reading from one of the very first paper scrolls. The Chinese recently invented the art of paper-making.

☞ Say "hello" to the young woman by the pond with a fan and a silk dress. Do not ask her how silk is made. She could be put to death if she tells you.

☞ Pass the cat and the acrobats. Stop and listen to the musicians. Entertainers often come to the house.

☞ Step across to the man using a brush dipped in ink. He is practising calligraphy – the art of writing.

☞ Follow the boy with a kite into the kitchen, where cooks are preparing a banquet. There's wild boar and bear's paws, game birds and fish, bamboo shoots and lotus roots.

☞ Hungry? Follow the dog out of the kitchen and enter the house. Kneel on embroidered cushions and eat from small bowls with chopsticks.

☞ **SEEK THE MAGIC HOURGLASS**
Now it is pale orange.

IN THE VALLEY OF THE KINGS

You are in Egypt, the kingdom on the banks of the River Nile. It is 1343 BC and this is the funeral of the young king Tutankhamun, who has died aged 18 years.

~ THE ROUTE ~

☞ Help carry the golden throne at the back of the procession. It has been made by skilled craftsmen in the Royal Workshops.

☞ Overtake the golden bed with lion heads. Egyptians believe in life after death so their possessions are buried with them.

☞ Pass the statue of a dog on a box. This is the god Anubis, who will protect the king's body. Egyptians worship many gods.

☞ Move ahead to the golden box on a sledge. It contains the king's liver, lungs, stomach and intestines preserved for his next life.

☞ Walk past the golden statue to the scribe sitting and writing on a papyrus scroll. Egyptians record events using pictures called hieroglyphs.

☞ See the king's body lying on a funeral boat. It has been made into a mummy – prepared with ointments and bandages – to preserve it for thousands of years.

☞ Step forward to meet the king's wife, Ankhesenamun. Only members of the royal family are considered good enough to marry the King. She may also be his niece or even his sister.

☞ Go past the king's model boat and on to the tomb entrance cut into rock. Kings used to be buried in pyramids. Now they are buried deep in the ground where no robber will find them.

☞ **SEEK THE MAGIC HOURGLASS**
Now it is pale orange.

CIRCLE OF STONE

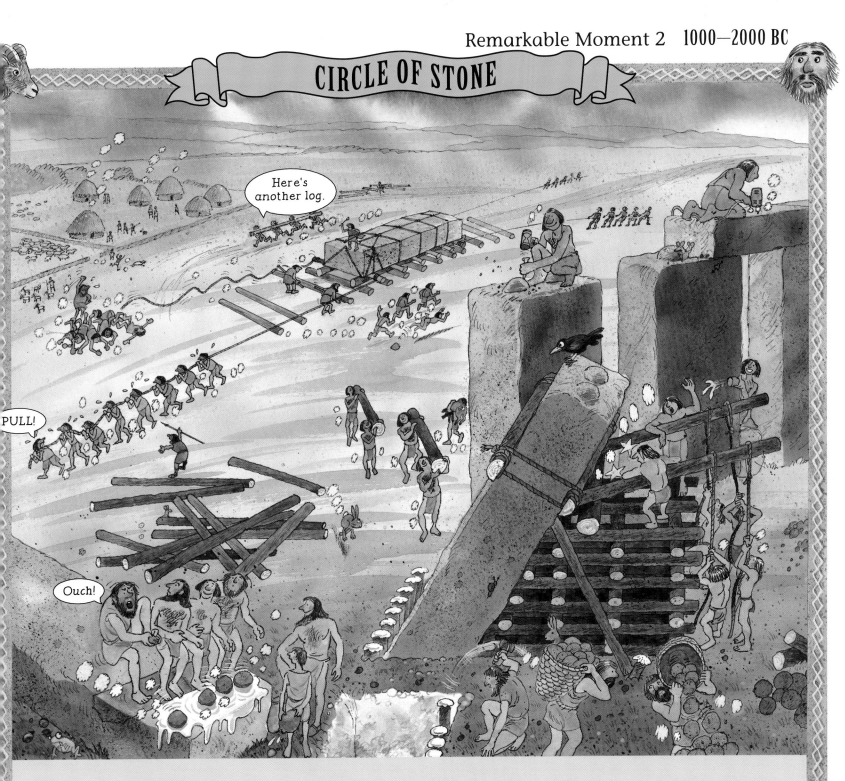

You have arrived in southern Britain during the early Bronze Age. Here people are building Stonehenge, a stone circle that may be used for religious ceremonies and astronomy. It will be built over several centuries.

~THE ROUTE~

☞ Find the group of huts. Most people live as farmers and herdsmen. They grow crops and keep herds of animals for food and clothing.

☞ Help pull a sandstone block called a *sarsen*. It weighs over 40 tonnes and has been dragged 32 km on rolling logs.

☞ Join the two men in front of the *sarsen*. They keep the logs in line as it moves forward.

☞ Find the four men who are dropping heavy stone balls on to the end of a *sarsen* to shape it. First they weaken the block with fire and water. This stone circle is unusual because the blocks are shaped.

☞ Jump over the deep pit being made ready for a *sarsen*. Borrow a hammer and drive in the stakes.

☞ Help men on timber scaffolding slide a *sarsen* into a pit. Feeling tired? Don't give up. A heavy crosspiece has still to be raised to the top.

☞ Climb up to the man at the top of a *sarsen*. He is shaping knobs that will fit into hollows made in the crosspiece. Skilled craftsmen are needed to build Stonehenge.

☞ **SEEK THE MAGIC HOURGLASS**
Now it is grey.

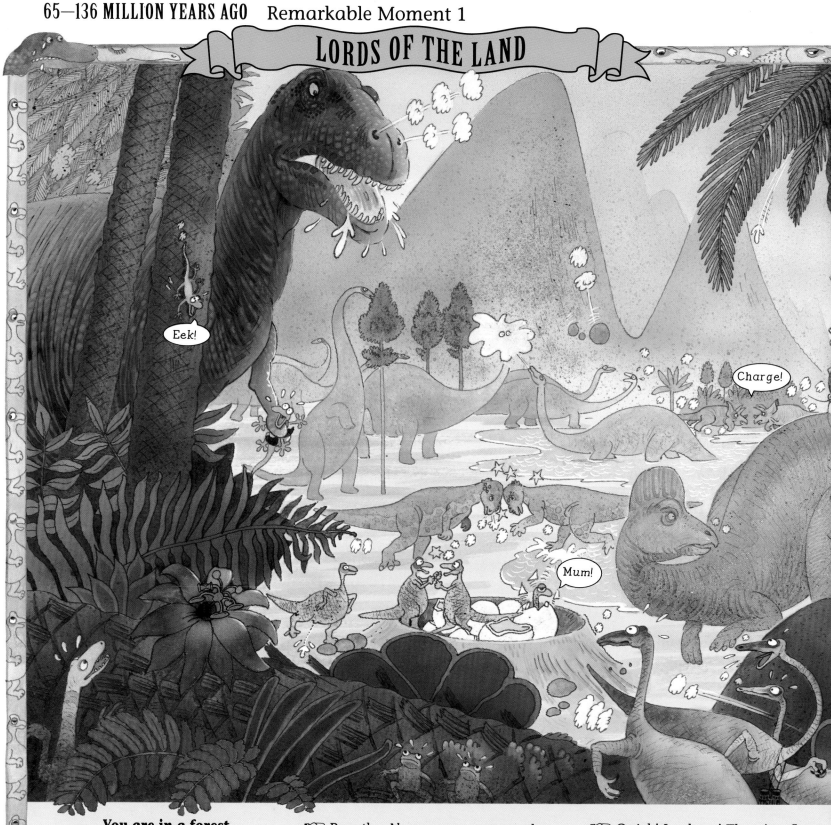

LORDS OF THE LAND

You are in a forest with the dinosaurs during the Cretaceous period.

☞ Find the nest of duck-billed baby *Corythosaurus*.

☞ Did you hear that crash? Two *Pachycephalosaurus* – "thick-headed lizards" – are butting their heads together.

☞ Pass the *Alamosaurus*, among the last of the giant plant-eating dinosaurs with long necks and small heads.

☞ Step across to two charging dinosaurs with horns. They are *Triceratops*.

☞ Follow the cockroaches down the tree to three ostrich-like dinosaurs – *Ornithomimus*. They can run as fast as racehorses. And they are about to run away now!

☞ Quick! Look up! There's a flurry in the trees and a mighty roar. Can you see that massive head above the trees and the huge curved fangs in its open mouth? It's the dreaded meat-eating *Tyrannosaurus rex*.

☞ See the lizard scamper down the tree. Leap across and hide with it among the first flowering plants in the world.

☞ **SEEK THE MAGIC HOURGLASS**
Now it is grey.

LORDS OF SEA AND SKY

You are swimming through the sun-warm seas of the Cretaceous period. Huge reptiles rule the sea and the sky.

~ THE ROUTE ~

☞ Find ammonites with coiled shells clinging to the rock under the water. These invertebrates – creatures without backbones – are food for the giant sea reptiles.

☞ Meet the *Elasmosaurus*, the reptile with paddles. It is swallowing stones to grind up food in its stomach.

☞ Quick! Dive away from the sharp teeth of the huge, shadowy *Ichthyosaurus* – "fish lizard". Members of its family have swum these waters for millions of years.

☞ Leap out of the water with the *Tylosaurus* – giant sea lizard. It is 9 m long.

☞ Ride on the back of the giant turtle, *Archelon*. Hold on tight!

☞ Hurry! Look up! *Quetzalcoatlus* are about to swoop for food! With a 12 m wingspan they are the largest flying creatures ever.

☞ Climb out of the water on the right. Dash along the shore and run for the safety of the hills.

☞ **SEEK THE MAGIC HOURGLASS**

Now it is pale blue.